RUB-A-DUB CUB

Written by Nora Gaydos
Illustrated by BB Sams

innovativeKids®

A cub.

A cub dug.

A cub dug up mud.

A cub dug up mud
in the sun.

YUCK!

Mud is stuck on the cub.

No fun!

A cub jumps in a tub.

A cub rubs in the suds.

Rub-a-dub-dub!

After You Read

Answer these questions about the story, and then use words from the story in fun, new ways!

1. What gets stuck on the cub?
   Why does the cub jump in the tub?

2. What other words rhyme with *cub*?
   What other words rhyme with *sun*?
   What other words rhyme with *dug*?

3. Make up a different sentence of your very own for each of these words: *mud, stuck, tub*.
   Now try to use all of those words together in one sentence!

Skills in This Story

Vowel sound: short *u*
Sight words: *a, in, the, is, on, no*
Word ending: *-s*
Initial consonant blend: *st*
Final consonant blend: *-mp*

STUCK DUCK!

Written by Nora Gaydos
Illustrated by BB Sams

The duck.

The plump duck.

The plump duck is stuck.

The plump duck is stuck
on a truck.

The plump duck is stuck on a dump truck.

The plump duck is stuck
on a dump truck with junk.

JUMP, DUCK, JUMP!

Bum luck!

The plump duck jumps
on a skunk.

The plump duck stunk!

After You Read

Answer these questions about the story, and then use words from the story in fun, new ways!

1. What kind of truck is the duck on?
   Why does the duck stink at the end?

2. What other words rhyme with *dump*?
   What other words rhyme with *junk*?
   What other words rhyme with *truck*?

3. Make up a different sentence of your very own for each of these words: *duck, stunk, plump*.
   Now try to use all of those words together in one sentence!

Skills in This Story

Vowel sound: short *u*
Sight words: *the, is, on, a, with*
Word ending: *-s*
Initial consonant blends: *pl, st, tr, sk*
Final consonant blends: *-mp, -nk*